Multicolor Problems

PART ONE OF *MATHEMATICAL CONVERSATIONS*

E. B. Dynkin and V. A. Uspenskii

Translated and adapted from the first Russian edition (1952) by

NORMAN D. WHALAND, JR., *and* ROBERT B. BROWN

SURVEY OF

RECENT EAST EUROPEAN MATHEMATICAL LITERATURE

A project conducted by

ALFRED L. PUTNAM *and* IZAAK WIRSZUP

Department of Mathematics,
The University of Chicago, under a
grant from the National Science Foundation

D. C. HEATH AND COMPANY BOSTON

Library of Congress Catalog Card Number: 63-19838

Introduction

On a geographical map different regions or countries are, for convenience, colored with different colors. Ordinarily, however, each region need not have its own separate color. It is sufficient to color with different colors only *neighboring* regions, that is, regions having a common boundary, such as regions S_1 and S_2 in Figure 1.[1]

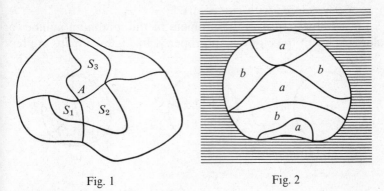

Fig. 1   Fig. 2

We shall use the following definition:

DEFINITION. *A* coloring of a map *is defined as* proper *if neighboring regions are colored with different colors.*

It is natural to ask, how many colors are needed to color a given map *properly?* Obviously, one answer is to use just as many colors as there are regions; in this case, we simply color each region with its own color. But we can hardly be satisfied with the solution. We are interested in the *minimum* number of colors sufficient for a proper coloring of a given map. It is easy to construct a map for which this minimum number of colors is two (Fig. 2).

The map in Figure 2 is the map of an island. The sea (shown by shading) surrounding the island is colored with neither color a nor color b. Usually, however, the sea is also colored on maps, so that

---

[1] The regions S_1 and S_3 are not considered to be neighboring. Although they come into contact at point A, they have no common *boundary.*

regions with a seacoast, that is, regions that border on the sea, must be colored differently from the sea. Consequently, for our purposes the sea is no different from an ordinary region. It does not matter that the sea is unbounded. Hereafter, therefore, we shall not consider the sea as separate, but shall instead include it among the other regions. Thus, the maps we shall consider hereafter will not be maps of islands, but will be thought of as extending over the entire plane. From this point of view, the map in Figure 2 can no longer be properly colored with two colors.

Let us now return to the problem of the minimum number of colors sufficient to color a map properly. In Figure 3 maps are rep-

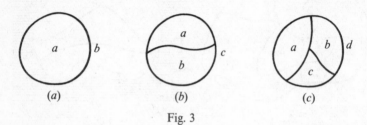

Fig. 3

resented for which these numbers are two, three, and four, respectively. But here our examples come abruptly to an end. Up to now, no one has been able to construct a map for which the minimum number of colors is five or more, in other words, which cannot be properly colored with four colors. It has been assumed that every map can be properly colored with four colors, but no one has yet proved it. (This is the famous *four-color problem*.) It has been proved, on the other hand, that every map can be properly colored with five colors. (This we shall prove in Chapter 4.) We are therefore able to make only the following two assertions, and we cannot fill the disappointing gap between them:

(1) *Not every* map can be properly colored with *three* colors (see Fig. 3c).

(2) *Every* map can be properly colored with *five* colors.

In the following chapters, we shall be concerned with questions about maps for which two colors (Chapter 1) and for which three colors (Chapter 2) are sufficient. In Chapter 3 we shall seek to deduce some criteria for coloring with four colors; in Chapter 4 we shall prove the *five-color theorem*.

2

1. Coloring with Two Colors

1. SIMPLE TWO-COLOR PROBLEMS

Problem 1.[1] Let n straight lines be drawn in the plane. Prove that the map formed by them can be properly colored with two colors (Fig. 4).[2]

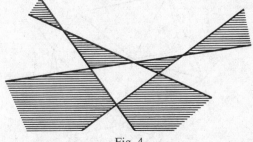

Fig. 4

Problem 2. Let n circles be drawn in the plane. Prove that the map formed by these circles can be properly colored with two colors (Fig. 5).

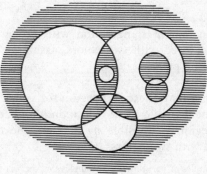

Fig. 5

---

[1] See the Preface for Instructions for the Use of This Book.

[2] *Hint.* A single straight line divides a plane into two parts; two parallel straight lines divide it into three parts; two intersecting straight lines divide it into four parts. All these maps can be properly colored with two colors. A proof can now be completed by mathematical induction.

DEFINITION. *If a plane is partitioned into triangles in such a way that any two triangles either have no common point, or have a common vertex, or have a common side, such a partition is called a* triangulation.[1]

DEFINITION. *If at the vertices of a triangulation the digits 0, 1, and 2 are placed in such a way that the vertices at the two ends of the same side are numbered with different digits* (Fig. 6), *such a* numbering *of vertices is called* proper.

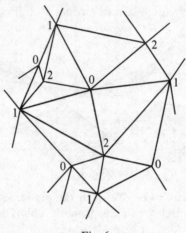

Fig. 6

Problem 3. Prove that a triangulation with proper numbering of vertices can be colored with two colors, assuming that it extends indefinitely over the plane.

Problem 4. If on a map there is a region for which the number of boundaries is not divisible by m, while the number of boundaries of each other region is divisible by m, then the map cannot be properly colored with two colors.

[1] Figure 7 shows examples of partitions into triangles that are not triangulations.

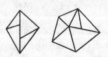

Fig. 7

2. PROBLEMS ON SQUARE BOARDS

The customary coloring of the squares of a chessboard serves as an example of a proper coloring provided we disregard the region outside. The problems on the chessboard that we introduce here will help us later on to solve the general two-color problem.

A knight can, under the rules of chess, go in one move from the square S to any one of the squares S_1–S_8 (Fig. 8). A rook can go in

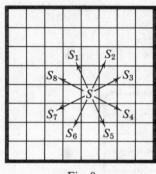
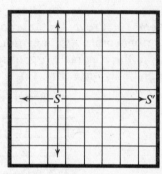

Fig. 8   Fig. 9

one move from square S to any square in the corresponding row or column (Fig. 9). In solving problems, we agree to regard a rook going from a square S to a square S' (Fig. 9) as visiting all the intervening squares as well.

Problem 5. With a knight, make the rounds of all the squares of a "chessboard" consisting of 5×5 squares in such a way that the knight lands on no square twice.

Problem 6. Number the squares of a 25-square "chessboard" in the order in which the knight rested on them in the previous problem. Shade all the squares that have an even number. Show what coloring results if the same operations are carried out, not on a 25-square "chessboard," but on one with an arbitrary number of squares, which a knight can visit as indicated in Problem 5.

Problem 7. Is it possible for a knight to touch once each of the squares of a 49-square board and on the last move to come to a square neighboring the square from which he started?

Problem 8. Prove that in one circuit a knight cannot visit all the squares of a 49-square board if he starts from the square S (Fig. 10).

Problem 9. A knight has made n moves and has returned to the square from which he started. Prove that n is even.

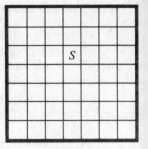

Fig. 10

Problem 10. Prove that a rook cannot move from corner A of a 64-square chessboard to the diagonally opposite corner B by visiting every square once and only once (Fig. 11).

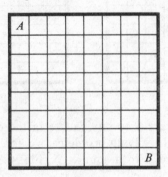

Fig. 11

3. PROBLEMS INVOLVING EVEN AND ODD NUMBERS

Problem 11. Can one arrange all 28 dominoes of a (double-six) set in a single chain so that the number 6 is at one end and the number 5 at the other?

Problem 12. Every human being who ever lived on the earth has, in the course of his life, shaken hands some completely definite number of times. Show that the number of human beings who have shaken hands an *odd* number of times must be *even*.[1]

Problem 13. At a meeting, 225 persons were present. Friends shook hands with each other. Prove that at least one of the participants present at the meeting shook hands with an *even* number of people.

[1] Zero is an even number; hence, a human being who has never shaken hands has shaken hands an even number of times.

Problem 14. In Figure 12, six points A, B, C, D, E, F are shown, and each of these points is connected with three of the remaining

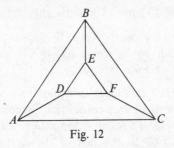

Fig. 12

five. Prove that if instead of six there are given only five points, then it is impossible to draw curves connecting them in such a way that each of the points is connected to exactly three of the remaining points.

4. NETWORKS AND MAPS

We shall now define several terms that we have been using intuitively up to now. Before doing so, let us consider an arbitrary network of curves in the plane and introduce a new term.

DEFINITION. *If from a particular point of this network one can move away along curves of the network in k different directions, then we shall say that the* multiplicity *of this point is k.*

For example, for the network represented in Figure 13, the multiplicity of the point A is 1, the multiplicities of the points B and

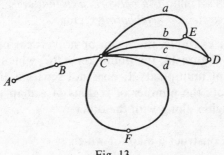

Fig. 13

F are each 2, the multiplicities of the points D and E are each 3, and, finally, the multiplicity of the point C is 7.

DEFINITION. *Any point of the network whose multiplicity is different from 2 is a* vertex *of the network.*

The network of Figure 13 has, by this definition, four *vertices, A, C, D,* and *E.*

DEFINITION. *The arc of any curve of the network between two adjacent vertices is called a* boundary.

In this way, each *boundary* contains two vertices. (In special cases, these two vertices can coincide to become one.) In our network (Fig. 13), there are seven boundaries: *ABC, ED, CaE, CbE, CcD, CdD,* and *CFC.* In the last of these, the two vertices containing between them the boundary *CFC* coincide. We shall denote the number of vertices of a network by v, and the number of boundaries by b.

Problem 15. Construct a network of curves for which
(a) $v = 3$, $b = 5$;
(b) $v = 7$, $b = 11$.

Problem 16. Let a network of curves have b boundaries and v vertices with the multiplicities $k_1, k_2, \ldots, k_v$. Prove that

$$k_1 + k_2 + \cdots + k_v = 2b.$$

Problem 17. Prove that in any network of curves the number of vertices having odd multiplicities is even.

Notice that not every network of curves can be called a *map*.

DEFINITION. *A* map *is a network such that every* boundary *must necessarily separate two neighboring regions.*

Hence, for example, there can be no vertices of multiplicity 1 on a *map*. In Figure 13, the boundary *ABC*, which goes out from the vertex *A* of multiplicity 1, does not separate any two *regions*. We shall denote the number of regions of a map by r and count the outside region along with the others.

Problem 18. Construct a map for which
(a) $v = 5$, $b = 8$, $r = 5$;
(b) $v = 11$, $b = 19$, $r = 10$;
(c) $v = 6$, $b = 12$, $r = 9$.

Problem 19. A map has b boundaries and r regions, which have $n_1, n_2, \ldots, n_r$ boundaries, respectively. Prove that

$$n_1 + n_2 + \cdots + n_r = 2b.$$

Problem 20. Prove that, in an arbitrary map, the number of regions having an odd number of boundaries is even.

Note. We have agreed to call *vertices* those points of a network of curves having a multiplicity different from 2. Sometimes, however, it is convenient to consider as vertices also certain points of multiplicity 2. As before, a boundary is a section of any curve lying between two successive vertices. For example, the map in Figure 14 has 9 vertices, $A, B, C, D, E, F, G, H, I$, and 11 boundaries, $AB, BC, CD,$ $DE, EG, GF, FA, BI, IH, HD, HG$. It is easy to verify that the statements and solutions of all the problems formulated earlier are still valid under the new meaning of *vertex*.

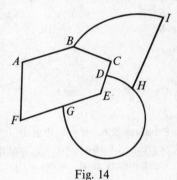

Fig. 14

5. GENERAL TWO-COLOR PROBLEMS

By analogy with the chessboard, we now introduce a rook on an arbitrary map. The rook goes through the various regions, being able to go in one move from any region into any neighboring one (in Fig. 15, from S to any one of S_1, S_2, S_3, S_4, S_5).

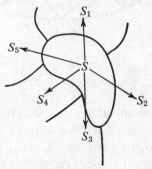

Fig. 15

Problem 21. With a rook, make a tour of all the regions of the map represented in Figure 16 without visiting any region twice. Number the regions in the order in which the rook visited them, and shade those regions that are given an even number.

Fig. 16

Problem 22. Prove that it is impossible for a rook to tour all the regions of the map represented in Figure 17 without visiting at least one region twice.

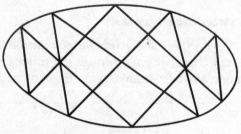

Fig. 17

Problem 23. Let a map be properly colored with two colors. Prove that all of its vertices have an even multiplicity.

Problem 24. Suppose all of the vertices of a map have an even multiplicity. A rook tours a series of regions (not necessarily all) of this map, without visiting any one of them twice, and returns to the region from which it started. Prove that the rook has made an even number of moves.

Problem 25. As in Problem 24, suppose all of the vertices of a map have an even multiplicity. A rook tours a series of regions of this map and returns to the region from which it started. (This time, in the process, the rook could have visited some regions more than once.) Prove that the rook has made an even number of moves.

Problem 26. Let all vertices of a map have an even multiplicity. Let a rook go along a certain path from the region S_0 to the region S_1 in p moves, and along another path in q moves. Prove that the numbers p and q are either both even or both odd.

Problem 27. Let all vertices of a map have an even multiplicity, including 2. Prove that the map can be properly colored with two colors (compare with Problem 23).

Problems 23 and 27 yield the following theorem, which completely solves the problem of the proper coloring of a map with two colors:

THEOREM. *A map can be properly colored with two colors if and only if all of its vertices have an even multiplicity, including 2.*

2. Coloring with Three Colors

6. A SIMPLE THREE-COLOR PROBLEM

Problem 28. Suppose n circles are drawn in a plane. In each circle let a chord be drawn so that chords of two different circles have at most one point in common. Prove that a map obtained in this way can always be properly colored with three colors. (Figure 18 is an example of such a map.)

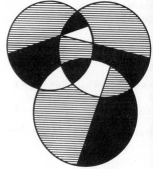

Fig. 18

7. PROBLEMS ON HEXAGONAL BOARDS

The hexagonal board pictured in Figure 19 has the same significance for the three-color problem that the chessboard has for the two-color problem. Unlike the ordinary chessboard, it is not composed of squares, but rather of regular hexagons, and can be properly colored with three colors, say white, black, and red[1] (Fig. 20), provided we disregard the region outside. For such a board, we could devise rules of play analogous to those for ordinary chess. We limit ourselves to introducing a playing piece that we shall call a *camel*.[2] In one move, the camel can go from a region in any of the three directions shown by arrows in Figure 19: up, down to the left, or down to the right; that is, it can go from region S to any one of the regions S_1, S_2, or S_3. In Figure 20, the path of a camel from the bottom corner of the board to the top, and from the top to the bottom is shown.

Our hexagonal board itself has the form of a hexagon. An "edge" of this large hexagon, or a "side" of the board, may consist of any number of hexagonal regions. (In Figure 19 a side of the board consists of five hexagonal regions.)

[1] In Figure 20, red is indicated by horizontal shading.

[2] The piece received this name in the school mathematics circles in Russia.

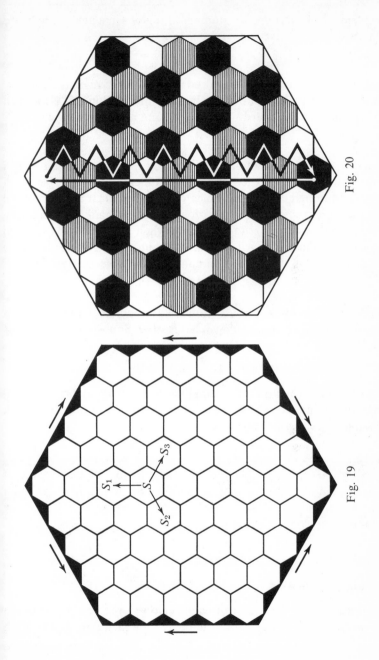

Fig. 20

Fig. 19

13

Problem 29. Determine the number of regions in a hexagonal board whose sides have five, six, and m hexagons.

Problem 30. Draw a hexagonal board with three regions on a side. Find a path for a camel starting in the center region and visiting all the regions on the board without touching any region twice.

Problem 31. Number all of the regions on the board in the order in which the camel touched them in Problem 30. Color black all regions numbered with multiples of 3, and red all regions whose numbers give remainder 1 when divided by 3. What kind of coloring results? What coloring do we obtain when we carry out the same process on another board, with a different number of regions on a side, that can be toured with a camel as indicated in Problem 30?

Problem 32. Suppose that a camel has made n moves and has returned to the region from which it started. Show that n is divisible by 3.

Problem 33. Prove that if a camel starts out from a corner region, it cannot tour a hexagonal board with three regions on a side, visiting every region only once.

Problem 34. Is it possible for a camel to tour all the regions of a hexagonal board with m regions on a side, touching each region only once, and arrive, on the last move, in a region neighboring the region from which it started?

8. DUAL DIAGRAMS

Let us mark the center of each region of the hexagonal board shown in Figure 19 and join the centers of each pair of adjoining regions by a line segment. If we erase the edges of the hexagonal regions, leaving only the centers and the line segments that connect them, we obtain the diagram in Figure 21. Points in Figure 21 correspond to regions of the board in Figure 19. The diagram we have drawn is very convenient for solving problems involving the path of a camel. (The directions in which a camel can move are shown by arrows.)

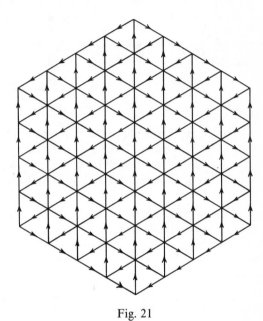

Fig. 21

Problem 35. Prove that it is impossible for a camel to tour all the regions of the hexagonal board in Figure 19 (or, what amounts to the same thing, all the points of the diagram in Figure 21) without visiting some region twice.

DEFINITION. *Diagrams related as are Figures 19 and 21 are* dual *to each other.*

A system of 25 points, connected by straight lines with arrows, is shown in Figure 22. A board *dual* to this diagram is shown

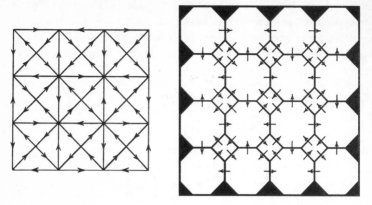

Fig. 22   Fig. 23

in Figure 23. This board is composed of regions of two kinds, octagons and squares. If we mark each octagon and each square at the center, join the centers of neighboring regions, and erase the boundaries of the regions, we obtain the diagram in Figure 22 again.

Problem 36. Devise a camel's tour of the diagram in Figure 22 so that no point is visited twice. Number the points of the diagram in the order in which they were touched and replace each number by its remainder when divided by 3. Color black all regions of the board in Figure 23 that correspond to points numbered 0 in Figure 22 and color red all regions corresponding to points numbered 1.

Problem 37. Prove that it is impossible for a camel to tour all of the regions of the board in Figure 23, touching each region only once, if it starts its tour in an octagonal region.

9. TRIANGULATION

We can consider the paths of camels on diagrams considerably more general than the diagrams shown in Figures 21 and 22. We recall that by a *triangulation* of a polygon we mean a decomposition into triangles, any two of which have either a vertex, a side, or no point at all in common (see first definition in section 1). Let us assume that some polygon (or even the whole plane) is triangulated, and that the triangles into which it (or the plane) is partitioned are properly colored with two colors, white and black (see, for example, Figure 24).[1] A playing piece that moves along the sides and vertices of the triangles, going in one move from any vertex to one of its *neighboring* vertices (that is, end points of the same side), will again be called a *camel*. Furthermore, the direction of motion will be such that, as the camel moves along a

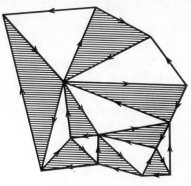

Fig. 24

side, a black triangle always lies to the right and a white one to the left. In Figure 24 the possible directions of a camel's motion are indicated by arrows.

Instead of referring to a special diagram, the following four problems, unlike the previous groups of problems, relate to arbitrary diagrams of the sort described.

Problem 38. Prove that a camel can go from any vertex of a diagram to any other.

Problem 39. Suppose a camel takes n steps and returns to its starting place. Prove that n is divisible by 3 (see Problem 4).

Problem 40. Let A and B be two arbitrary vertices of a diagram. A camel can go from point A to point B in different ways. Let p be the number of moves in one of these ways and q the number of moves in another (Fig. 25). Prove that $p - q$ is divisible by 3.

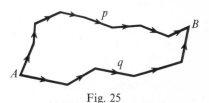

Fig. 25

---

[1] Notice that here the outside (sea) is not one of the regions by the definition of triangulation. It cannot be either white or black. However, if we annex a black triangle to each white one bordering on the "sea," then the "sea" can be white even though it is not a "triangle."

Problem 41. Let a polygon or the plane be triangulated, and let the triangles of the division be properly colored with two colors. Prove that the vertices of all of the triangles can be numbered with the digits 0, 1, and 2 in such a way that any two neighboring vertices have different digits (compare with Problem 3).[1]

The number of colors necessary for a proper coloring of a map is obviously not in the least dependent on the size of the regions or on the shape and length of the boundaries. It is determined only by the relative positions of the regions, boundaries, and vertices. If we draw a map on a sheet of rubber and stretch this sheet unequally (without ripping it), all maps thereby obtained from the original map are completely equivalent to one another from our point of

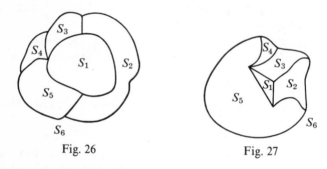

Fig. 26   Fig. 27

view. For example, the two maps in Figures 26 and 27 are equivalent.

In the formulation of Problems 3 and 41, the maps were said to be made from triangles with straight sides. The solution of these problems is unchanged, however, if we consider maps with curved sides instead of straight ones. Hence, the result of Problem 41 can be formulated in the following way:

THEOREM. *Let a map consist of regions which have three boundaries each.[2] If this map can be properly colored with two colors, then its vertices can be properly numbered with three digits.*

The result of Problem 3 can be generalized in the same way. The solution remains exactly the same, since two neighboring triangles

---

[1] Recall our definition of *proper* numbering of vertices in section 1.

[2] We shall call such regions *triangles;* in general, we shall call a region with n boundaries an *n-gon*.

18

have, as before, different orientations, although they can now border one another in two different ways (Fig. 28a and b).

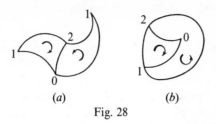

(a)   (b)

Fig. 28

10. DUAL MAPS

Consider the map in Figure 29. Inside each of its regions mark a point, the capital of the region. Let us connect the capitals of each pair of neighboring regions by a railroad (dotted lines in Figure 29),

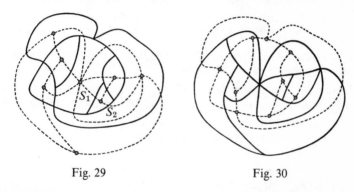

Fig. 29   Fig. 30

which does not go outside these two regions nor through any vertex. If any two regions have several boundaries in common, as, for example, the regions S_1 and S_2 in Figure 29, we join the two capitals by several railroads, one through each common boundary. In doing this, we take care to see that two different railroads do not cross one another.

If we replace the dotted lines on our map by solid lines, and the solid lines by dotted lines, we obtain the map shown in Figure 30. The original map and the map of the railroad lines exchange roles; the original map is the railroad map for its own railroad map. Consequently, the two maps in Figure 29 (or in Fig. 30), one drawn with dotted lines, the other with solid lines, play a completely symmetric role—each of them is the railroad map for the other.

We shall call two such maps *dual maps*,[1] defined as follows:

DEFINITION. *A map is said to be the* dual *of a second map if the two maps play completely symmetric roles, one to the other, under the following conditions:*

(1) *Each boundary of one map intersects exactly one boundary of its dual map.*

(2) *In the interior of every region of one map, there is exactly one vertex of its dual map. (In this way, a one-to-one correspondence is set up between the elements (regions, boundaries, vertices) of two dual maps,[2] such that regions of one map correspond to vertices of the dual, vertices correspond to regions, and boundaries to boundaries.)*

(3) *Neighboring regions of one map correspond to neighboring vertices of the dual map, and vice versa.*

(4) *If one of the vertices of one map has multiplicity k, then the region in the dual map corresponding to this vertex has k boundaries; that is, according to our convention, it is a k-gon.*

If we now try to construct railroad lines for arbitrary maps, we encounter difficulties of two kinds.

In the first place, it is possible that the diagrams of railroads do not represent maps at all in our sense. We consider, for example, the diagram of railroads for the map shown in Figure 31 (this diagram is drawn separately in Figure 32). In this diagram, there exist

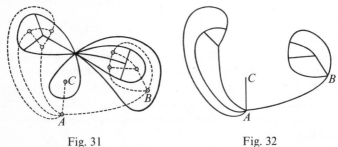

Fig. 31   Fig. 32

---

[1] The construction by which we obtained the map in Figure 21 from the map in Figure 19 differs from the method we have just used only in that there we did not take the exterior region into account. Hence, to obtain the map dual to the map in Figure 19, it is sufficient to add a single vertex to the map in Figure 21, joining it to all of the outside vertices of that map. The same can be said of the maps shown in Figures 22 and 23.

[2] That is, each element in one map corresponds to a single well-determined element of the dual map.

"boundaries" (*AB* and *AC*) which do not separate regions; one and the same region lies on both sides of each of these boundaries.

Also, the diagram of railroads for the map shown in Figure 33 represents a true map, but the exterior region of the railroad map

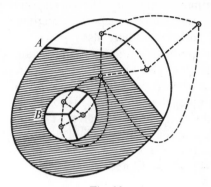

Fig. 33

contains two vertices, *A* and *B*, of the original map. In this case, there is no duality between the original map and its railroad map.

The second difficulty can be avoided if we consider only *connected* maps.

DEFINITION. *A map is* connected *if no one region separates the remaining regions into two or more groups that are nowhere contiguous.*

In other words, if we draw a connected map on a sheet of paper, then, no matter what region we cut out with a pair of scissors, the remaining part does not fall into separate pieces. The map shown in Figure 33 is not a connected map. (The "separating" region is shaded.) A connected map can also be defined as a map in which any given vertex can be reached from any other vertex by moving along the boundaries of the map.

We could overcome the first difficulty in the same way as the second by simply excluding from consideration maps for which this difficulty arises. But instead we shall introduce maps similar to the "maps" in Figure 32, that is, maps with boundaries that do not separate regions. In what follows, we shall almost never encounter such maps; they are introduced here only so that our *duality principle* is not violated.

We now formulate the *duality principle* for connected maps.

(*a*) The railroad map of a connected map is again a map; moreover, it is a connected map.

(*b*) Every connected map is the railroad map of its own railroad map.

Hence, a connected map and the corresponding railroad map are dual to each other, and the important relationships between the duals we named earlier hold here also.

However, for condition 4 on page 20 to remain true, we need the following modification: every boundary not separating regions must be counted twice when computing the number of boundaries of a region. For example, the region in Figure 34 is an octagon (the multiplicity of the corresponding vertex A of the dual map is 8). With this stipulation, the results of all of the problems in which the number of boundaries of regions was to be determined remain true, as, for example, Problems 19 and 20.

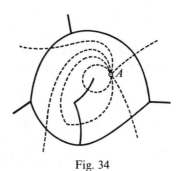

Fig. 34

We can now state the following result, which follows directly from condition 3 of dual maps:

THEOREM. *If the regions of a map can be properly colored with n colors, then the vertices of the dual map can be properly numbered with n numbers. Conversely, if the vertices of a map can be properly numbered with n numbers, the regions of the dual map can be properly colored with n colors.*[1]

---

[1] Notice that it is meaningless to speak of a proper coloring of a "map" containing boundaries which do not separate regions. In fact, in such a map there is a region that lies on both sides of one of its boundaries, that is, a region neighboring itself. See the Definition in section 4.

11. NORMAL MAPS IN THREE COLORS

DEFINITION. *A* normal map *is a map all of whose vertices have multiplicity 3.*

Figure 35 shows an example of a normal map. The significance of normal maps will be made clear in Chapter 3.

Fig. 35

Problem 42. Prove that a normal map can be properly colored with three colors if and only if the number of boundaries of each of its regions is even.

It should be noted that the theorem formulated in Problem 42 does not completely solve the problem of proper coloring with three colors, since it holds only for normal maps.

3. The Four-Color Problem

12. NORMAL MAPS IN FOUR COLORS

In this chapter, we shall consider the question of coloring maps with four colors. (Of course, we shall not succeed in settling this question completely.)

In solving the general four-color problem, it is sufficient to consider *normal maps;* for, if we can properly color all normal maps with four colors, then we can also properly color all maps in general with four colors. Indeed, if we have a vertex with multiplicity greater than 3 in an arbitrary map, we can draw a small circle around the vertex, remove all of the boundaries in the interior of the circle, and adjoin its interior to one of the adjacent regions (Fig. 36). We then

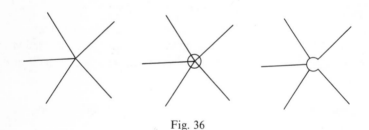

Fig. 36

obtain some normal map. If this map can be properly colored with four colors, this will obviously be true of the original map also. Hence, in what follows we shall consider only normal maps.

Up until now we have considered only proper colorings of the regions and proper numberings of the vertices of maps. We now introduce proper numbering of boundaries. Two boundaries are said to be *neighboring* if they have a vertex in common.

DEFINITION. *A numbering of boundaries is called* proper *if any two neighboring boundaries have different numbers.*

Figure 37 shows an example of a *proper* numbering of boundaries.

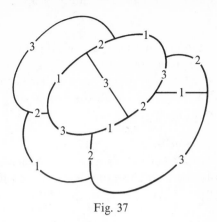

Fig. 37

13. VOLYNSKII'S THEOREM

The four-color problem is equivalent to the problem of properly numbering boundaries with three digits. This equivalence is established by the following theorem.

VOLYNSKII'S THEOREM.[1] *A normal map can be properly colored with four colors if and only if its boundaries can be properly numbered with three digits.*

The proof of this theorem follows from Problems 43 to 45. In the following, it will be convenient to number regions with four numbers rather than to color them with four colors. For this purpose we choose the number-pairs (0,0), (0,1), (1,0), (1,1). These pairs can be added termwise, and, in order to use no other number-pair in the process, we replace sums by their remainders after dividing by 2. For example,

$$(1,0) + (1,0) = (0,0),$$
$$(0,1) + (1,1) = (1,0).$$

[1] V. V. Volynskii (1923–1943) was a talented young mathematician, a student of the department of mechanics and mathematics of Moscow State University. He fell at the front in World War II.

Volynskii's Theorem was actually discovered in the nineteenth century by the Scottish physicist and mathematician P. G. Tait (1831–1901). See P. G. Tait, "Remarks on the Colouring of Graphs," *Proceedings of the Royal Society of Edinburgh,* vol. 10 (1880), p. 729.

Problem 43. Prove that if a normal map can be properly colored with four colors, then its boundaries can be properly numbered with three digits.

Problem 44. Let the boundaries of a normal map be properly numbered with the three number-pairs (0,1), (1,0), (1,1). A rook visits a series of regions of this map and returns to its starting point. Prove that the sum of the numbers of all the boundaries crossed by the rook is equal to (0,0).

Problem 45. Let the boundaries of a normal map be properly numbered with three number-pairs. Prove that this map can be properly colored with four colors. (This completes the proof of Volynskii's theorem.)

Problem 46. Let the number of boundaries of each region of a normal map be divisible by 3. Using Volynskii's theorem, prove that this map can be properly colored with four colors.

At the end of the following section, after the reader will have learned about Euler's theorem, the four-color problem will be solved for maps with fewer than twelve regions.

4. The Five-Color Theorem

14. EULER'S THEOREM

The boundaries of some region can fall into separate, disconnected contours (Figs. 38a and b). In this case, however, as is ob-

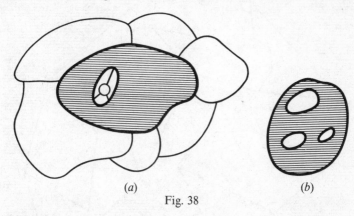

(a)   (b)

Fig. 38

vious from the figures, the region necessarily separates the remaining regions into at least two groups that are nowhere contiguous; hence the map is *not connected*.

If we limit ourselves to the consideration of *connected maps,* the boundaries of each region form a closed contour. This closed contour is similar to the perimeter of a polygon with straight sides, differing only in that the pieces between vertices are generally curved. (At individual points this contour can touch itself, as shown in Fig. 39.) By using this similarity between the regions of a connected map and ordinary polygons, we prove the celebrated theorem of Euler.[1]

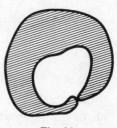

Fig. 39

[1] Leonhard Euler (1707–1783), one of the greatest mathematicians, was a member of the St. Petersburg Academy of Science from 1727 to 1741 and from 1766 to the end of his life, and of the Berlin Academy of Sciences from 1741 to 1766.

EULER'S THEOREM. *If r is the number of regions, v the number of vertices, and b the number of boundaries of a connected map, then*

$$r + v = b + 2.$$

Proof. We first prove this theorem for maps of polygons whose sides are straight line segments. The sea in such a map is the outside of the polygon (in Fig. 40 the sea is shaded).

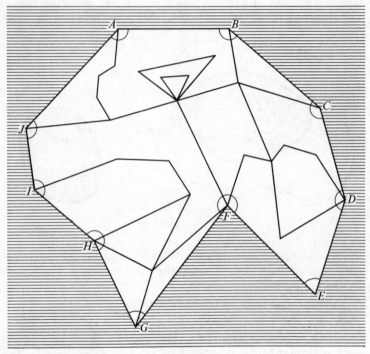

Fig. 40

Let us calculate the sum of the interior angles of all polygons in our map. The number of polygons is $r - 1$ (all regions except the sea). If a polygon has n sides, then, as is well known, the sum of its interior angles is $(n - 2) \cdot 180°$. Hence, the sum of the interior angles of all the polygons is

$$T = (n_1 - 2) \cdot 180° + (n_2 - 2) \cdot 180° + \cdots + (n_{r-1} - 2) \cdot 180°,$$

where $n_1, n_2, \ldots, n_{r-1}$ are the numbers of sides of our polygons.

This sum is equal to

$$T = [n_1 + n_2 + \cdots + n_{r-1} - 2(r-1)] \cdot 180°.$$

Let b_e be the number of outer boundaries (lying next to the sea), and b_i be the number of interior boundaries (not lying next to the sea). Then

$$b = b_i + b_e$$

(in Fig. 40, $b_i = 32$, $b_e = 10$). By Problem 19,

$$n_1 + n_2 + \cdots + n_{r-1} + b_e = 2b,$$
$$n_1 + n_2 + \cdots n_{r-1} = 2b - b_e.$$

Hence,

$$T = [2b - b_e - 2(r-1)] \cdot 180°.$$

We now calculate the same sum T in another way. Let v_i be the number of interior vertices and v_e be the number of vertices at the sea (in Fig. 40 $v_i = 19$, $v_e = 10$). Obviously,

$$v = v_e + v_i$$

and

$$b_e = v_e.$$

The sum of the interior angles of the polygons at each interior vertex is $2 \cdot 180°$. Hence, the sum of the interior angles of all the polygons, except those angles whose vertices are at the sea, is $2 \cdot 180° \, v_i$. To obtain T, we must add to this sum all the angles lying at the sea (they are marked in Fig. 40), in other words, the sum $(v_e - 2) \cdot 180°$ of all interior angles of the polygon $ABC \ldots J$. Thus,

$$T = 2 \cdot 180° \, v_i + (v_e - 2) \cdot 180°$$
$$= (v - v_e) \cdot 2 \cdot 180° + (v_e - 2) \cdot 180°$$
$$= (2v - v_e - 2) \cdot 180°.$$

If we set the two expressions for T equal to each other, we get

$$[2b - b_e - 2(r-1)] \cdot 180° = [2v - v_e - 2] \cdot 180°,$$
$$2b - b_e - 2(r-1) = 2v - v_e - 2.$$

Since $b_e = v_e$, it follows that

$$2b - 2(r-1) = 2v - 2,$$
$$b - r + 1 = v - 1,$$
$$r + v = b + 2.$$

We now consider the general case, in which the regions can have curved boundaries also. As before, let v be the number of vertices, r the number of regions, and b the number of boundaries. On the boundaries, we introduce new, auxiliary vertices of multiplicity 2 (in Fig. 41 the vertices A, B, C, D, E, F, G, H, I). In this way, we

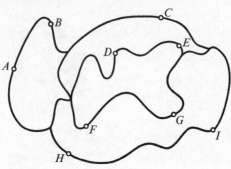

Fig. 41

obtain as many new boundaries (the pieces of old boundaries between the new vertices) as there are new vertices. Now we replace each curved boundary in the new map by a straight line segment with the same end points. If we place the auxiliary vertices sufficiently close together (we can introduce arbitrarily many of these vertices), these line segments will not cross. We obtain a new map (the dotted lines in Fig. 42), all of whose regions are polygons with straight

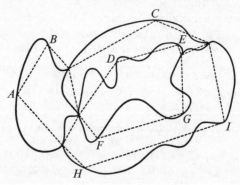

Fig. 42

sides. If the number of auxiliary vertices is equal to v' and the number of new boundaries is equal to b', then the total number of vertices in the new map is equal to $v + v'$ and the total number of boundaries is equal to $b + b'$. The number of regions, however, remains the same. As has just been proved, Euler's theorem holds for the new map; that is,

$$(v + v') + r = (b + b') + 2.$$

Since

$$v' = b',$$

we have

$$v + r = b + 2,$$

Problem 47. Let six points be given in a plane. Let every point be joined to four other points by curves that do not intersect. Prove that all the regions of the resulting map are triangles.

Problem 48. Let seven points be given in a plane. Prove that it is impossible to join them with nonintersecting curves in such a way that each point is joined with exactly four other points. (Use the result of Problem 4.)

Problem 49. Given three houses and three wells, prove that it is impossible to connect every house with every well by nonintersecting paths.

Problem 50. Given five points in a plane, prove that it is impossible to join every point with every other point by nonintersecting curves.

Problem 51. Prove that there cannot exist a map containing five regions with the property that every two neighbor each other.

Problem 51 suggests that four colors are sufficient for the proper coloring of any map. The proof of the five-color theorem is based on the result of this problem. Obviously, in the proof of this theorem, vertices of multiplicity two can be excluded from consideration. In Problems 52 to 54 we shall assume that the multiplicity of any vertex is at least three.

Problem 52. Prove that in any connected map in which any of the vertices has a multiplicity of at least three, there exists a region with fewer than six boundaries.

15. THE FIVE-COLOR THEOREM

Problem 53. Prove that *every map can be properly colored with six colors.*[1]

Problem 54. Prove the FIVE-COLOR THEOREM: *Every map can be properly colored with five colors.* (Use the result of Problem 51.)

We can solve the four-color problem for a special case with the methods used in the solution of the five-color problem. This is done in Problems 55 and 56. Exactly as in the problem on five colors, we assume that the map under consideration contains no vertex of multiplicity 2.

Problem 55. Prove that the inequality

$$b \leq 3r - 6$$

holds for connected maps in which the vertices have multiplicities of at least 3.

Problem 56. Prove that *any map with less than twelve regions can be properly colored with four colors.*

---

[1] It is assumed that the map has no boundaries that do not separate regions (see Definition in section 4).

Concluding Remarks

Problems—such as multicolor problems—about the properties of figures and solids which do not change under arbitrary deformations, in which the figures and solids are not torn or glued together, belong to a particular branch of mathematics called *topology*. Topology, which is one of the youngest branches of mathematics, developed into a distinct mathematical discipline about the turn of the last century. A leading role in the development of topology in the last thirty years has been played by the Soviet topological school, whose most prominent representatives are P. S. Urysohn (1898–1924), P. S. Alexandroff (1896–   ), and L. S. Pontryagin (1908–   ).

The reader can find accounts of questions having to do with Euler's theorem and multicolor problems in the following works whose presentations differ from this book's:

Rademacher, H., and Toeplitz, O. *Enjoyment of Mathematics.* Princeton, N. J.: Princeton University Press, 1957.

Hilbert, D., and Cohn-Vossen, S. *Geometry and the Imagination.* Translated by P. Nemenyi. New York: Chelsea Publishing Company, 1952.

In the latter book, problems of map-coloring on surfaces more complicated than the plane are solved. The reader will also find some elementary material on topology in it.

An elementary introduction to topology is presented in the book:

Arnold, B. H. *Intuitive Concepts in Elementary Topology.* Englewood Cliffs, N.J.: Prentice-Hall, Inc., 1962.

Selected research articles are listed in the Bibliography on page 66.

Appendix

COLORING A SPHERE WITH THREE COLORS

Suppose that a sphere[1] is divided into a certain number of domains; in other words, suppose a map is drawn on a sphere. We can ask if there exists a region containing antipodal points, that is, two diametrically opposite points of the sphere. If there are four regions, it is possible that no region exists that contains antipodal points (Fig. 43). If the number of regions exceeds four, then it is all

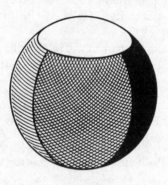

Fig. 43

the more true that such a region need not exist. On the other hand, if there are only two regions in the map, then at least one of them will contain both end points of a diameter of the sphere.[2] Indeed, it can happen that every such pair of points belongs to the boundary of both regions. An example is a sphere divided into two hemispheres.

---

[1] By a sphere we mean the *surface* of a ball.

[2] To prove this, it is sufficient to consider an arbitrary point A on the boundary between the two regions. Its antipodal point A' belongs to one of the regions. Since A belongs to that same region (a point on the boundary we consider as belonging to both adjacent regions), A and A' form the desired pair of points.

The question now arises, what about the case of three regions? We shall prove that here, as with two regions, there is always a region containing a pair of diametrically opposite points. Further, a far more general assertion can be proved.

THEOREM. *If a sphere is divided into an arbitrary number of regions (greater than two), and these regions are arranged in three groups in an arbitrary manner, then there exist two diametrically opposite points belonging to regions of the same group.*[1]

For clarity, we shall assume that the regions of each group are colored the same color: for example, the regions of the first group, blue; those of the second group, black; and those of the third group, red. A pair of diametrically opposite points belonging to regions of the same group we shall call *identically colored.*

Proof. We prove the theorem by contradiction. Assume that a map K drawn on a sphere is colored with three colors, and that no pair of diametrically opposite points lie in regions of the same color.

This assumption leads to a contradiction in the following way: We prove that from every three-color map with no identically colored pairs, a new map can be constructed that again contains no identically colored pairs, but has fewer regions than the first map. Thus, if we start off with the map K, whose existence we have assumed, we can construct a map K_1 with fewer regions and containing no identically colored pairs. Then from the map K_1 we can construct a map K_2 by the same method, and so on. We obtain an infinite sequence of maps

$$K, K_1, K_2, K_3, \ldots, K_m, \ldots,$$

none of which contains identically colored pairs. If we let n be the number of regions in the map K, n_i the number in K_i, then

$$n > n_1 > n_2 > n_3 > \cdots > n_m > \cdots.$$

Thus, we obtain an infinite decreasing sequence of positive integers, which is impossible. The exposition here of such a proof leads us to the following definition.

DEFINITION. *The* method of infinite descent *is a proof by contradiction, using an infinite decreasing sequence of positive integers.*

[1] This theorem was discovered (in a much more general form) by the Soviet mathematicians L. A. Lyusternik and L. G. Shnirelman.

Thus, still attempting to prove the theorem by contradiction, again let an arbitrary map K, containing no identically colored pairs, be given. A map K_1 must be constructed, again containing no identically colored pairs, but consisting of fewer regions than the map K.

Note that if the map K is not properly colored, that is, if it contains boundaries between regions of the same color, then we can immediately obtain the desired map K_1 by erasing these boundaries. Therefore, we shall consider henceforth only properly colored maps K.

We use the following lemma to prove our theorem.

LEMMA. *In a map with more than two regions, a point diametrically opposite a boundary point is an interior point; that is, it lies strictly inside some third region.*

Proof. Indeed, in a *properly colored* map of more than two regions, every boundary point belongs to at least two differently colored regions. For example, let a boundary point A belong to a red and a blue region; then its antipodal point A' can belong neither to a blue nor a red region. Therefore, it lies strictly within a black region (as according to the lemma).

Proof of the theorem, continued. Applying the lemma to the proof of the theorem, we let B be a point lying on the boundary of some region, colored red, say. We move from the point B along the boundaries of the map in such a way that red regions are always on our left (Fig. 44).[1] We continue until we return to a point C

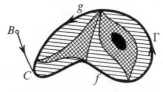

Fig. 44

that we have already touched. We now consider the closed non-intersecting contour $CfgC$ (Fig. 44), which we denote by Γ. We shall draw the map on the sphere separately for the "northern" and "southern" hemispheres. We assume, for clarity, that the con-

[1] In Figures 44, 46, and 47 red is indicated by horizontal shading, blue by cross-hatching.

tour Γ lies wholly in the northern hemisphere (Fig. 45). For the general case, the proof is unchanged. Now we construct a contour

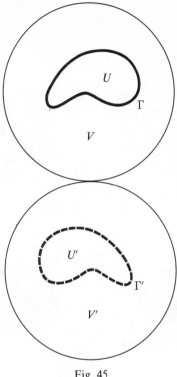

Fig. 45

Γ', consisting of the points diametrically opposite the points of the contour Γ (Fig. 45). By the lemma, the contour Γ' consists only of interior points, that is, it cuts none of the boundaries of the map. In particular, it does not cut the contour Γ, which is formed from boundaries.

The contour Γ divides the sphere into two parts, U and V (Fig. 45). In exactly the same way, Γ' divides the sphere into parts U' and V', where U' consists of points diametrically opposite those of U, and V' consists of points diametrically opposite those of V. Since Γ and Γ' do not intersect each other, the contour Γ' lies in one of the parts U or V. If in V, then the contour Γ lies in V'.

Since the contour Γ' does not cut any boundary of the map, it lies entirely inside some region. All points of the contour Γ belong to the red regions; hence, no point inside or on the contour Γ' can be red. To be specific, we can assume that this region is colored black (Fig. 46).[1] In this case, no point of the contour Γ can belong

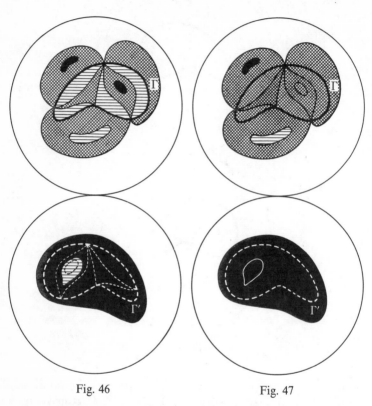

Fig. 46   Fig. 47

to a black region; in other words, all boundaries from which the contour Γ is formed are boundaries between blue and red regions. Since only red regions lie on one side of the contour Γ, then only blue regions lie on the other side (the map is properly colored). Suppose that red regions lie on the side U and blue ones on the side V, as in Figure 46. If now we change the color of all regions in U to blue, so that blue regions border on both sides of the contour Γ (Fig. 47), then at the same time all regions in U' remain black.

[1] In Figure 46 the dotted lines consist of points diametrically opposite to boundary points in the region U.

(Notice that no identically colored pairs occur in this coloring, since, first of all, the points in U have become blue and their antipodal points in U' black and, secondly, all other points, as well as their antipodal points, have not changed color.) Now let us erase the contour Γ and all boundaries lying inside U and U'. The number of regions is thereby decreased (since the contour Γ separated at least two regions from one another).

Thus, from an arbitrary map K containing no identically colored pairs, we have constructed a map K_1, which has fewer regions than the map K and, likewise, has no identically colored pairs. The method of infinite descent is used once more as in the first part of this proof, and our theorem is proved by contradiction.

Solutions to Problems

PROBLEM 1. We shall prove this theorem by mathematical induction. Assume the theorem already proved for n straight lines. We shall prove that it is then also valid for $n + 1$ straight lines. Let us consider a map K formed by $n + 1$ straight lines, and erase one of these lines, say the line l. We then have a map K^* formed by only n straight lines, which, according to the assumption, can be properly colored with two colors. We color this map, K^*, in black and white. We then replace the erased line l. It divides the plane into two parts, each of which is properly colored with two colors (Fig. 48a). We now leave the colors

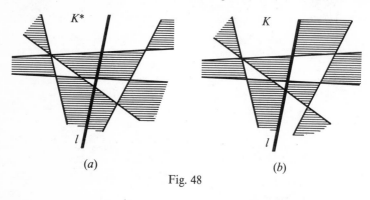

(a)   (b)

Fig. 48

of all the regions in one of the two parts unchanged, while in the other part we replace black by white and white by black (Fig. 48b). Each half-plane herewith remains properly colored. If two neighboring regions of the map K be in different half-planes, they bound one another along a segment of the straight line l. The new regions are formed by the dissection of some region of the map K^* by this straight line. In this case also, each two neighboring regions of the map K are colored in different colors. The theorem is valid for $n = 1$; according to what we have proved, it is valid for $1 + 1 = 2$ straight lines, for $2 + 1 = 3$ straight lines, etc.; thus, it is valid for any given number of straight lines.

PROBLEM 2. This problem can be solved by the method of mathematical induction, exactly as Problem 1 was solved. Instead of proceeding in this way, however (the reader can do it as a useful exercise), we shall carry out the following plan. For each of the regions into which the plane is divided, we count the number of circles within which it lies. (For the map in Fig. 5 the results of such counting are shown in Fig. 49.) We note that the numbers for any two neighboring regions always differ by 1. In fact, if two neighboring regions A and B are separated by the arc of a circle C, then one of the regions lies inside C and the other outside C; and the regions A and B either both lie, simultaneously, inside or else both lie, simultaneously, outside every circle other than C. It is sufficient, therefore, to color all the even-numbered regions with one color, and all the odd-num-

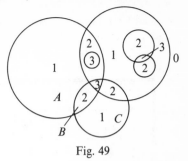

Fig. 49

bered regions with another color, in order to obtain a proper coloring of our map.

PROBLEM 3. In such a numbering of vertices, at the three vertices of each triangle the three digits, 0, 1, 2 will appear. We draw arrows along the sides of the triangles from 0 to 1, from 1 to 2, and from 2 to 0. In this way, each triangle receives a definite orientation. One can distinguish two types of triangles: triangles with clockwise orientation (Fig. 50) and triangles with

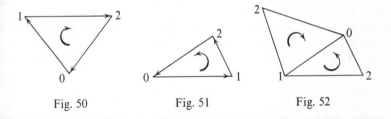

Fig. 50   Fig. 51   Fig. 52

counterclockwise orientation (Fig. 51). We color all triangles of the first type white and all those of the second type black. Since any two neighboring triangles always have opposite orientations (Fig. 52), we shall obtain a proper coloring.

PROBLEM 4. We assume the contrary, and color our map *properly* with white and black. Suppose that in this way we obtain k white regions having $n_1, n_2, \ldots, n_k$ boundaries, and l black regions having $n_1', n_2', \ldots, n_l'$ boundaries. Each boundary belongs to exactly one white and one black region; if b denotes the total number of boundaries, then

$$b = n_1 + n_2 + \cdots + n_k = n_1' + n_2' + \cdots + n_l'.$$

All but one of the numbers $n_1, n_2, \ldots, n_k, n_1', n_2', \ldots, n_l'$ is divisible by m.

41

It then follows, from this equality, that *all* the numbers of boundaries must be divisible by m, and this proves our premise by contradiction.[1]

PROBLEM 5. In Figure 53 the squares are numbered in the order in which the knight goes around them.

7	12	17	22	5
18	23	6	11	16
13	8	25	4	21
24	19	2	15	10
1	14	9	20	3

Fig. 53

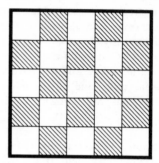

Fig. 54

PROBLEM 6. See Figures 53 and 54. We have obtained a proper coloring of the 25-square chessboard. In the same way, we obtain a proper coloring of any other board, such that the knight can make the rounds of all the squares touching each one only once, and coloring the even-numbered squares all one color. Suppose such a board is already properly colored with two colors, as may always be done.[2] Then the knight jumps from a square of one color to a square of the opposite color on each move. Therefore, if all the squares are numbered in the order in which the knight touches them, all squares with even numbers will be of one color, black, say, and all squares with odd numbers will be of the second color, white, say. To reverse the procedure, if, on an uncolored but numbered chessboard, we color all the regions with even numbers black, and all the regions with odd numbers white, we simply revert to the previous coloring, which is a *proper* coloring.

[1] Suppose, to be specific, it is n_1 that is not divisible by m. Since $b = n_1' + n_2' + \cdots + n_l'$ and $n_1', \ldots, n_l'$ are all divisible by m, b must be divisible by m. But then, since $n_1 = b - (n_2 + \cdots + n_k)$, and $n_2, \ldots, n_k$ are all divisible by m, n_1 must be divisible by m. Here is a contradiction of the supposition that n_1 is not divisible by m; therefore, here the theorem is proved.

[2] While it is true that every chessboard can be properly colored with two colors in the customary checkerboard design, it is not true of every chessboard that a knight can make the rounds of all the squares so as to touch each square only once. A 2×2 chessboard is obviously such an exception. Find another one.

PROBLEM 7. No, it is impossible. Let us color the board properly with two colors, then number the squares in the order in which the knight made the rounds of them. The first square has the number 1; the last, the number 49. They ought, therefore, to have the same color, as do all the squares with odd numbers (see the solution to the preceding problem). But two neighboring squares in a proper coloring are colored differently.

PROBLEM 8. Let us color our board properly with two colors, and in such a way that the square S is colored white (Fig. 55). If a knight could tour the board starting from the square S, then, numbering the squares in the order of passage, we would have assigned the odd numbers 1, 3, ..., 49 to the white squares (compare with the solution of Problem 6). The number of white squares would thus be 25. But in all there are actually only 24 white squares, as Figure 55 clearly indicates.

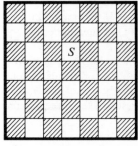

Fig. 55

PROBLEM 9. With each move, the knight changes the color of his square. Therefore, when he reaches a region of the same color as the one from which he started (in the given case he has reached the actual square from which he started), he has made an even number of moves.

PROBLEM 10. Each of the rook's moves can be replaced by a series of simple moves, each of which is a move from a square to a neighboring one. With each such simple move, the rook changes the color of its square. In a tour of the whole board of 64 squares, it will make 63 simple moves, an odd number. Hence, the last square it reaches must have a color different from that of the square where it started, while the squares A and B have the same color.

PROBLEM 11. Impossible. A domino consists of two halves, each half bearing one of the seven numerals 0, 1, 2, 3, 4, 5, 6. There are as many dominoes as there are possible pairs of these numerals. Each numeral thus occurs eight times, six times with other numbers, and twice more on one domino, a double, on which the number is combined with itself. In the chain of dominoes, two dominoes are joined together so that the two touching halves bear identical numerals. Hence, each numeral occurs an even number of times, say n, in the interior of the chain, and 8 − n times on the ends, also an even number of times. Consequently, every number either appears at neither end (and zero is an even number), or at both ends at the same time.

PROBLEM 12. Let N be the total number of human beings who ever lived on earth, and let m be the number of handshakes they have exchanged. Number all human beings, and denote by n_k the number of times the kth human being has shaken hands. If the kth human being has shaken hands with the lth, then this handshake is included once in the number n_k and again in the number n_l. Hence, in the sum

$$S = n_1 + n_2 + n_3 + \cdots + n_N \quad (N \text{ summands}),$$

each handshake is counted twice and

$$S = 2m.$$

But, if the sum of any group of numbers is even, as here, then there must be an *even* number of odd summands.

PROBLEM 13. If all participants in the meeting shook hands with an odd number of friends, it would follow that each of the 225 persons (225 is an odd number) had shaken hands an odd number of times. This contradicts the result of the preceding problem (with $N = 225$).

PROBLEM 14. If this were possible, then from each point there would emanate three curves. If we multiply by 3 the number of points, here 5, we would be counting each curve twice (since each curve has two end points) and would thus obtain double the number of curves, an even number. But $5 \cdot 3 = 15$, an odd number.

PROBLEM 15. One possible solution for (a) is exhibited in Figure 56, and a solution for (b) is drawn in Figure 57.

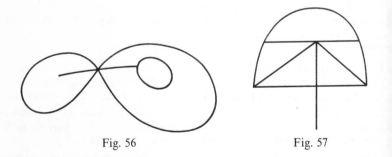

Fig. 56   Fig. 57

PROBLEM 16. In the sum $k_1 + k_2 + \cdots + k_v$ each boundary is counted twice, since it is counted in the multiplicity of each of its end points. (If the end points of a boundary coincide, the boundary is counted twice in determining the multiplicity of that end point.)

PROBLEM 17. The statement follows from Problem 16. Indeed, if the sum of some numbers is even, then the number of odd summands occurring must be even.

PROBLEM 18. Possible solutions for (a), (b), (c) are shown in Figures 58, 59, 60, respectively.

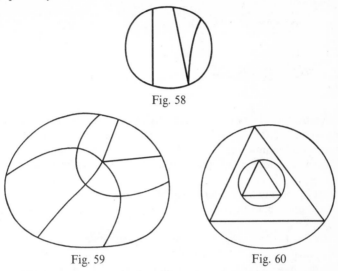

Fig. 58

Fig. 59   Fig. 60

PROBLEM 19. Every boundary is counted twice in the sum $n_1 + n_2 + \cdots + n_r$, since it belongs to two neighboring regions.

PROBLEM 20. This follows from Problem 19 in exactly the same way that Problem 17 follows from Problem 16.

PROBLEM 21. See Figures 61 and 62.

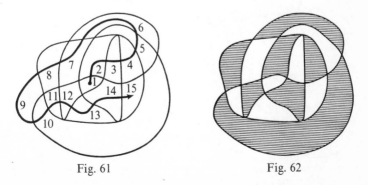

Fig. 61   Fig. 62

PROBLEM 22. Let us properly color our map with two colors (Fig. 63). If we number the regions in the order in which they are toured, all regions with

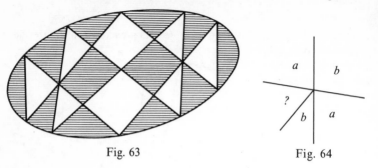

Fig. 63   Fig. 64

even numbers will be of one color, and all with odd numbers of the second color (see the solution of Problem 6). In all, there are 21 regions, of which 11 must have odd numbers (1, 3, ..., 21), and 10 have even numbers (2, 4, ..., 20). At the same time, however, there are 12 black and only 9 white regions.

PROBLEM 23. If any vertex has an odd multiplicity, then even the regions surrounding it cannot be properly colored with two colors (Fig. 64).

PROBLEM 24. Let us consider the path of our rook (the dotted line in Fig. 65). We now erase part of the map lying outside the path, and adjoin the path itself to the map. We obtain a new map (Fig. 66). All interior vertices of this map have, by assumption, an even multiplicity, while the outer vertices, formed by the intersection of the boundaries of the old map with the path of the rook, all have multiplicity 3. There will be an even number of vertices having odd multiplicities (Problem 17); therefore, the rook must have crossed

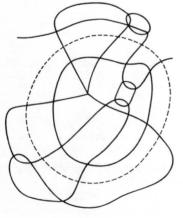

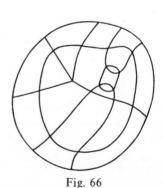

Fig. 65   Fig. 66

46

over an even number of boundaries or, what amounts to the same thing, it has made an even number of moves.

PROBLEM 25. The case of the rook starting out from S_0 and visiting each region not more than once has already been considered in Problem 24. Suppose now that the rook has visited some region S_1 twice, that is, it has crossed its own path in this region (Fig. 67). Let the number of moves in the segment S_0aS_1 be p, the number in S_1bS_1 be q, and the number in S_1cS_0 be r. We have to prove that $p + q + r$ is even. By problem 24, q is even. The path $S_0aS_1cS_0$ also satisfies the conditions of Problem 24; hence $p + r$ is likewise even. From this it follows that $p + q + r$ is even. If, on the other hand, the rook makes two loops instead of one (Fig. 68), then, by erasing one of them, S_1bS_1, for example, we obtain the case just considered. An even number of moves, again by Problem 24, is made in going around the loop S_1bS_1; hence, an even number of moves will be needed for the entire path with S_1bS_1 included. In this way, we can prove our statement for an arbitrary number of loops.

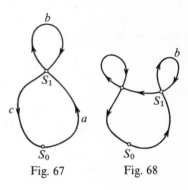

Fig. 67   Fig. 68

PROBLEM 26. If the second path is traversed in the opposite direction, then we go from S_1 to S_0 in q moves. Therefore, if we go from S_0 to S_1 along the first path, and then from S_1 to S_0 along the second path in the reverse direction, we return to S_0 in $p + q$ moves. By Problem 25, $p + q$ is an even number, whence p and q are either both even or both odd.

PROBLEM 27. *First method.* Let us start out with the rook from some region S_0, and traverse all the regions of the map, one after another. We number them in the order in which the rook has visited them. It may happen that some regions are visited twice, or even oftener. Any such region is assigned, not one number, but two or more numbers. By Problem 26, however, the numbers assigned to any one region will be either all even or all odd. On the other hand, neighboring regions must have numbers that differ by an odd number. In fact, if region S_1 can be reached from S_0 in p moves and if S_2 borders on S_1, then S_2 can be reached from S_0 in $p + 1$ moves. This means that every path leading from S_0 to S_2 consists of a number of moves that is even if $p + 1$ is even, and odd if $p + 1$ is odd; therefore, this number is even if p is odd, and odd if p is even. If, after the rook has visited all regions of the map, we color with one color all regions with even numbers, and use a second color for all regions with odd numbers, then we obtain a proper coloring.

Second method. We shall travel over the boundaries and vertices of our map. In the process, we always leave from a vertex along a boundary different from that on which we arrived. Since there are no vertices of multiplicity 1 on our map, having arrived at an arbitrary vertex, we can always go out from it. We continue along in this fashion until we reach, for the first time, a vertex already met before, say the vertex A. The part of our path traversed in going out from the vertex A and returning to it forms a closed contour that does not intersect itself; we erase this from our map. In consequence, the multiplicity of each vertex either is not altered (if the contour does not pass through it) or is decreased by 2 (if the contour does pass through it). Some vertices of multiplicity 2 may thereby vanish, but, as before, the multiplicity of any vertex remains even. On the newly obtained map, we again single out some closed contour which consists of boundaries and does not intersect itself, and we likewise erase it. We continue the process until the whole map has been erased. One can, consequently, obtain a map all of whose vertices have even multiplicities by laying on top of one another these closed contours, each of which divides the plane into two parts. This map is entirely analogous to the map in Figure 5, which is obtained by the superposition of circles. Exactly as in Problem 2, we can prove that such a map can be properly colored with two colors.

Remark. With the help of analogous considerations, it is not difficult to show the following. We can draw a map, all vertices of which have even multiplicities, with one stroke of the pen, that is, without lifting the pen from the paper or tracing over any boundary twice. In general, we can draw a network of curves in one stroke of the pen in only two cases, either if all of its vertices have even multiplicities, or if exactly two of the vertices have odd multiplicities. (In the latter case we must, however, begin the stroke in one of these two vertices and end in the other.)

PROBLEM 28. To solve this problem, we can either use induction (see Problem 1) or apply the method used in the solution of Problem 2. We give here an outline of the proof by the second method. We select any one of our figures (a circle with a chord). It divides the plane into three parts. We number all regions of the map that lie in one of these parts, 0; all that lie in the second part, 1; and all that lie in the third part, 2. We do this for all the figures. Each region will then have n numbers. We add them and find the remainder after division by 3. The regions for which this remainder is 0, we color white; those for which the remainder is 1 or 2, we color red or black, respectively. It can now be shown, exactly as in Problem 2, that the resulting coloring is proper.

PROBLEM 29. Let a side of the board be made up of m hexagons. We remove the $6(m - 1)$ regions lying on the six sides of the board. We then obtain a board of the same form, but whose sides consist of only $m - 1$ hexagons.

Hence, if we denote the number of regions of the board with m sides by S_m, then

$$S_m = 6(m - 1) + S_{m-1}.$$

In exactly the same way,

$$S_{m-1} = 6(m - 2) + S_{m-2},$$
$$S_{m-2} = 6(m - 3) + S_{m-3},$$
$$. . . . .$$
$$S_2 = 6 \cdot 1 + S_1,$$
$$S_1 = 1.$$

From this, it follows that

$$S_m = 6(m - 1) + 6(m - 2) + \cdots + 6 \cdot 1 + 1$$
$$= 1 + 6[1 + 2 + \cdots + (m - 2) + (m - 1)].$$

But[1]

$$1 + 2 + \cdots + (m - 2) + (m - 1) = \frac{(m - 1)m}{2}.$$

Therefore,

$$S_m = 1 + 6 \frac{(m - 1)m}{2} = 3m^2 - 3m + 1.$$

PROBLEM 30. See Figure 69.

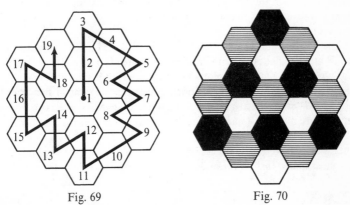

Fig. 69   Fig. 70

PROBLEM 31. We obtain a proper coloring in three colors for a board each of whose sides contains three hexagons (see Fig. 69 and 70).[2] We obtain the

[1] See, for example, I. S. Sominskii, *The Method of Mathematical Induction* (Boston: D. C. Heath and Company, 1963).

[2] In Figure 70 red is indicated by horizontal shading.

same result on an arbitrary board. In fact, assume that we have a board already properly colored with three colors.[1] In this case, the camel goes from red regions to white, from white to black, and from black to red (compare with Fig. 19 and 20). If the camel begins its path in the central red region, and we write down the sequence of colors of the regions through which it moves, we obtain the sequence (r = red, w = white, b = black):

$$rwb \quad rwb \quad rwb \quad rwb \quad rwb \quad \ldots .$$

Hence, regardless of the path the camel takes (assuming, however, that the path begins in a red region and that the second region is colored white), all regions whose number is divisible by 3 will be black, and all regions whose number gives a remainder of 1 or 2 when divided by 3 will be red or white, respectively.

Thus, the coloring described in the formulation of Problem 31 coincides, in fact, with the initial proper coloring of the hexagonal board (compare with Problem 6).

PROBLEM 32. For example, if the camel begins its path in a black region, then the sequence of the colors of the regions through which it passes will be (see the previous problem)

$$brw \quad brw \quad brw \quad b.. \quad \ldots .$$

The period of this sequence consists of three terms; therefore, the camel can reach a region of the same color as the region from which it started (in particular, it can reach the actual region from which it started) if and only if the number of moves it has made is divisible by 3.

PROBLEM 33. To tour a board with 19 regions (see Fig. 70), the camel must make 18 moves, that is, a number of moves which is a multiple of 3, and arrive at a region of the same color as that from which it started. Hence, it will have passed through more regions of this color than regions of the other two colors. However, there are no more regions colored like the corner region than there are regions of each of the other two colors (see Fig. 70).[2]

PROBLEM 34. To tour a board of $3m^2 - 3m + 1$ regions (see Problem 29), a camel must make $3m^2 - 3m = 3(m^2 - m)$ moves, and since the number of

---

[1] It is easy to see that a hexagonal board can always be properly colored with three colors. For instance, it is possible to apply the coloring of Figure 70 to a small section of the board and then to extend it in the obvious way to cover the entire board.

[2] On the contrary, there are more red regions than white or black. Hence Problem 30 does have a solution.